A WOMAN WITH A GRUDGE

by
Catherine Scott

Best wishes

Catherine Scott
x

Published by Paul Gibson
www.paul-gibson.com

Printed by Dolman Scott
www.dolmanscott.co.uk

Cover design by Angela Bell
www.angelabellartist.co.uk

Book layout by Ian Halstead
www.ianhalstead.com

First Published in 2019
ISBN 978-0-9957846-2-8

ACKNOWLEDGEMENTS

Welcome to my fourth collection. This book has been two years in the making and I'm equally excited about this one as I have been about my previous three. I sincerely hope you enjoy it.

Thank you to:

My family and friends for their support and encouragement.

Angela Bell for the amazing cover.

Lou Duffy-Howard and Monty Martin for their reviews.

Richard Duffy Howard for the picture of me on the back cover.

Paul Gibson and Ian Halstead for the design and publishing.

CONTENTS

Prosy Thoughts

Trumped Up Thoughts

Friendly Thoughts

Serious Thoughts

Sad Thoughts

THOUGHTS FROM HULL

When Hull won the City of Culture Bid for 2017, the council replaced
the old cracked pavers in the city centre with some brand spanking new
beautiful, granite ones. Within days they were spattered with chewing gum.
I want to ban the stuff.

Paved with Gum

No-one shops in Hull anymore
They go to Leeds or Meadowhall
M & S have closed and Hammonds have gone
And the streets of Hull are paved with gum

Whitefriargate has gone downhill
It needs a regeneration pill
It used to buzz, it used to hum
But sadly now it's paved with gum

In twenty seventeen the future looked bright
When Hull was awarded the Turner Prize
But The City of Culture has now become
The city where streets are paved with gum

And I'm sad for Hull because it's got the potential
To be categorically influential
It's got The Docks, it's got The Marina
It's got museums and several theatre
It's got Dead Bod, it's got The Ferens
And some fantastic, original, brilliant musicians
So there are lots of reasons for the tourists to come
But they don't right now because we're paved with gum

I hate to see my city snubbed
I want it clean, I want it scrubbed
I want the gum off the streets, I want the rubbish in the bins
I want the buskers out with their violins

I want Hull to thrive, I want it to prosper
I want Maureen Lipman to win an Oscar
I want the tourists to come and spend their brass
I want Hull to kick some ass
I want people to come and go home raving
'You should go to Hull and see their paving
They've really got their act together
They've been photographed in the altogether'

I so want to believe, to believe in Hull
I want to believe it's possible
For Hull to be brave and stand alone
And declare our city a no-gum zone
For if we abolished slavery and we survived the Blitz
Surely to goodness we can manage to do this

HS2

'Get out of my way,' screams The HS 2
'I'm way more important than any of you
I'm bright, I'm shiny, I'm special, I'm new
I'm the future, I'm progress, I'm The HS2'

I don't give a monkeys about the homes being lost
Or the businesses claiming they've been ripped off
Frankly they can whistle for their compensation
My only concern is the destination

By 2026 I shall have my own line
I'll shave twenty minutes off the commuting time
Between London and Birmingham I shall toot my toot
I'm costing billions and I don't give a hoot

I'll be bagging every serious commuter
As they climb aboard with their fancy computer
Conducting conferences via the wonder of the web
Hunched over lap tops without a word being said

And when in the evening they arrive back home
Crumpled, exhausted still glued to their phone
They'll be thanking God for that extra time
For the twenty minutes shaved off their commuting time

For that twenty minutes a day they can spend with their kids
That twenty minutes a day for their families
That twenty minutes a day to spend counting their cash
That twenty minutes closer to a heart attack

Do you think it's possible that all along
The powers that be have had it wrong?
Do you think they feel guilty about the people they've crossed
Whose homes and businesses are sure to be lost?

Do you question the necessity for the HS2?
Believe me you would if you came from Hull
Our trains are worn out but we keep making do
Whilst they swank it up about their HS2

And did you hear about our rejected application
For the Hull to Selby line electrification?
There's been too many broken promises
And now we're saying, 'WHAT ABOUT US?
We're watching you and we are serious
It's time you spent some money on us.'

I wrote this just as all the hoo haa about Brexit was starting to kick off.
Time moves on…or does it?

Double Trouble

To rhyme or not to rhyme
That's the dilemma
Some say it is better to have tried to rhyme and failed
Than never to have tried at all
It's a lot of fuss about nothing much
All that caring, all that effort, amounts to nothing
For still Labour lost
Corbyn, Corbyn, where were you Corbyn?
You may yet achieve success
Such stuff do we dream

Methinks Theresa doth protest too much
A poor player, who, mehopes, will soon be heard no more
Barred from the food bank
As she listens to the music play on

Boris, a dandelion by reputation
And full of bullshit
Well known for his lies and indiscretions
Gove, true to himself, took the dagger and stabbed Boris in the back

Double Trouble, Double Trouble
May and Johnson Spit and Bubble

Fellow poets and good people of Hull
Be aware it will soon be March 2019
And compared to the heat of summer madness
The next winter will be long and cold
Be assured the future will be dull as tarnished brass
There will be dissatisfaction and anger
No handouts for the poor
Mounting debt and hunger
Shout, 'Chaos! And lock up the Tory Fat Cats!'

I'd give my eye teeth
For all to end well

Summat Aht There?

I don't know much about the Universe
The Galaxies, Solar systems or the geology of the Earth
I leave that to the scientists
Who persist
With their theory that somewhere out there, other intelligent life exists
But as a realist
I ask, 'where's your evidence? Where's your proof?'
I'm dismissed… 'Pooooof…
My dear…you simply don't understand …the Universe is so huge'

And they waffle on for hours about the theory of probability
Steadfastly
Refusing to even consider the possibility
That it just might be
That I'm Right
And that earth has the only living creatures of any kind, anywhere
And that there never has been and never will be, anything, 'out there'

And I wonder what Hullensians would make of such a discovery?
My guess is these wonderful, ever plain speaking, say-it-like-it-is, down to
earth people would exclaim
'Well tell me summat I don't know. I mean to say, it's common sense int it?
We could 'av told 'em that years ago and saved 'em the trouble
An' the money
Research…Pfff…I ask yer

Anat th'end o' day nowt's changed 'as it?
We've still gorra feed bairns an' pay lecky 'ant we?
An' speaking for mesen, I'm glad, 'cos nah,
Perhaps council'll stop messin' abaht
And get their priorities right
An' gerron wi' sortin' them pot 'oles aht

…Summat aht there? Don't think so mate.

Tha'll be saying earth's rhand next!'

Ić

Ibrahimovic
Modrić
Matić

There's lots of ićs
On the pitch
But Hull City haven't had an ić
They've lacked an ić
And we so, so needed an ić

They've had a ticklyić
An annoyingić
An irritatingić
A can'treachitić
A bumić
A crotchić
A fannyić
And a dickić

But what they've really needed is
A 'stickitinthebackofthenetić'
A 'scratchittillitbleedsić'
A 'hungryforitrununtilyoudropić'
A 'someonetomakethefanscheerić'

But now they've got an Ić
At last they've got an Ić
They've only gone and signed David Milinković
Fingers crossed hemakesthenetić

I wrote this in utter frustration when our holiday in Crete turned out to be less than successful and a complete wash out.

Fucking Crete

It's fucking Crete it's 6.00 a.m
And the fucking bin men are here again
Fucking clanging, fucking banging
Fucking dragging, fucking slamming
Bastards

It's fucking Crete, it's fucking pouring
It's fucking Crete, it's fucking boring
The meals are shit, the telly's crap
The fucking blokes are fucking fat
Bastards

It's fucking Crete, no fucking laughs
No fucking jokes, no fucking gaffs
The hotel's fucking understaffed
We're reduced to playing fucking drafts

It's fucking Crete we're fucking stuck
It's fucking Crete, we're fucking fucked
It's fucking Crete, it's fucking dull
We wish we'd stayed at home in Hull

NAUGHTY THOUGHTS

Mary

The ladies' group seemed quite refined
Polite conversation, gentle and kind
Their speakers were 'nice' but inexorably boring
With their holiday snaps and long-winded talking
There was no fizz, no bounce, no boom
They needed a kick up their va va voom

Enter Mary energetic and keen
Who made an impression by sweeping clean
Under her guidance and with new ideas
The ladies group moved up a few gears
And although the membership was initially wary
They concurred it was better with fun loving Mary

She invited women from all walks of life
To give interesting talks on their styles of life
First to arrive… a ventriloquist
Who was quickly followed by a sex therapist
Then a drag queen, a wrestler, a contortionist
These and more were on Mary's list

But behind closed doors a few tongues wagged
Eye brows were raised and questions were asked
'Do you think?' 'I'm not sure,' 'Could she possibly be?'
'She's certainly different, I think you'd agree'
'There's something about her,' 'I really don't know'
They analysed Mary blow by blow

At the end of her term wearing sequinned tights
Mary gave a speech on human rights
She spoke with courage she spoke with passion
Of her difficult trans into women's fashion
And many amongst them shed a tear
As she described a life of abject fear

For her story with a few rang quite a bell
Because they too had lived through hell
They knew about judgement, of simply not fitting
Of being tempted but never quite quitting
They'd endured the loneliness, pain and despair
Whilst trying to conform to the 'norm' out there.

Then Brenda (who was known for being reflective)
Brought the disclosure into perspective
She spoke for them all as she summed it up
'You're better off here with folk you can trust
You have no need of those hypocrites
With their small-minded attitudes and behaviour like dicks

Many of us here have a shady past
But never has one of us has been known to grass
You wouldn't believe the things we've done
A few of us are on the run
And at the end of the day when push comes to shove
We stick together, we're the sisterhood
So well done Mary, you've joined the team
Of naughty old ladies who are living the dream'

Don't

Allow your mind to wander, allow your eyes to roam
Do not email, do not text, don't answer the telephone
Don't listen to the radio, don't play your new CD
Do not play computer games, don't watch a DVD

Don't put in the washing, forget you said you'd bake
Likewise with the ironing and the bed you meant to make
Don't worry about the cleaning or the shopping or the kids
And should they say they're hungry let them help themselves to crisps

Don't walk the dog, don't answer the door
Don't pick the bits up off the floor
Don't clean the windows, don't shop for food
Forget your caring attitude

Don't wash your hair, don't make an effort, don't attempt to look your best
Just doss around in a pair of pants, a dressing gown and vest
They'll get a shock when they walk in they'll say 'Jesus, what the fuck…?'
And you will simply tell them that today you've 'given up'

You tell them in a voice so flat there is no intonation
That all you ever wanted was a bit of recog-nation
You don't attempt to justify or explain your 'strange' decision
You just sit back, relax, observe and await juxtaposition

The family are in a flap, what on earth is going on?
Where's their tea, their fresh clean clothes, and the ironing not done!
Of necessity they club together and arrange a takeaway
You order a Chicken Korma and make it clear it's them who'll pay

While Shauny irons and Miffy cleans, the power is subtly shifting
A significant change hangs in the air because you are doing nothing
You have given up the rat race, the chores and all that stuff
For today you have decided you don't give a flying fuck

Dear Ladies of the W.I.

I am The Mistress of all Preserves
You should taste my chutneys and lemon curds
My marmalades, mincemeats, jams and jellies
My pickled eggs and bottled berries
My kitchen shelves are stacked and heaving
With Kilner jars from floor to ceiling

So you'd think with my culinary expertise
That apple pie would be a breeze
But I can't make pastry for the life of me
Short crust is a mystery
I try very hard but I can't get it right
So I'm going to pick your brains tonight
I'm relying on you to help me out…

You see I've got company coming and they're all such snobs
They wear Chanel and low cut tops
They brag their cake is simply gorgeous
They witter on about their sauces
Their sponges, casseroles, roasts and quiche
They create each dish with apparent ease
So you see, I feel a bit…well… inadequate…

So, Dear Ladies of the W.I.
A few tips please for my apple pie
For I'm very keen I want to impress
I'm sorry?… I missed that? Did you suggest?
I attempt an apple crumble instead?
Or failing that go to M & S?
Because, after all, that's what they do…
Oh really? Well I never! I hadn't a clue…

Thank you, Dear Ladies of the W.I.
For your sound advice re. my apple pie
I don't need friends who falsely boast
About their quiches and their roasts
When frankly not a-one compares
To my marmalades, chutneys and lemon curds

I'm going to teach those snobs a lesson
When they gather at mine for a bitching session
When they tut together about my mistakes
I'm going to yell, 'you're a load of fakes
I've seen you shopping in M & S
For your apple pies and your delicatesse
It's time you learned a little finesse
So tonight it's poetry with Catherine S......Enjoy!'

I wrote this poem after watching a TV programmed entitled, 'The Sex Robots are Coming.' The programme followed a man who had a female sex robot, the final straw for me came at the end when he was asked, 'if you had to choose between your wife and the robot, which would you choose?' After about two seconds hesitation he said, 'the Robot'

Sad Man

Soon, ladies, we won't need to worry about ever having sex again
Because some right weirdos have invented female sex robots for men
So whenever the urge takes them it's there for the taking
Sex on a plate – robotic love making

The robotic girl is young and curvaceous
She whispers all the right words in all the right places
The robotic girl puckers her lips
She ticks all the essentials on the sad man's list

The robotic girl fulfils his needs
The robotic girl unlocks her knees
She's ready for sex anytime, anywhere
She tickles his fancy everywhere

There's no need for foreplay, no need for respect
No need for him to emotionally connect
No need for kindness, no time for fun
The robotic girl puts lead in his gun

But sad man's life has now backfired
She's not performing as required
Seems her guarantee's expired
She desperately needs to be rewired

The sad man turns and pleads with his wife,
To help him out in his hour of strife
'Of course I will,' she feigns delight...
She'll have his balls for dinner tonight

She leads him on, she plays their song
She pulls him up, they smooch along
She closes the door, turns the key
'Tonight', she smiles, 'just you and me'

Patiently she bides her time
Offers him a glass of wine
Serves a slice of chocolate cake
He takes a bite...big mistake

The sad man's wife is no-one's fool
The sad man's wife plays it cool
She makes the bed, lays out her tools
Sadomasochism rules!

Like a lamb to the slaughter he danced the dance
From the very start he stood no chance
She lured him through into the kitchen
Sad man never knew what hit him

Some hours later she made the call
'My husband is not well at all
'Please come at once he's barely breathing
I'd say he's taken quite a beating'

The Paramedics arrived complete with kit
Though none of it compared to his
A ball and chain, a whip, a mask
High heels, stockings, lipstick and basque

The Paramedics suppressed a laugh
They nudged each other, 'just look at that'
The sad man's wife played the scene
She wept and dabbed on Germolene

At the funeral she sat at the back
Demurely attired in designer black
The sad man's wife had taught her new phrases
She called them all out in the all the wrong places

Robotic girl has now been retired
The Merry Widow is greatly admired
For taking a stance against the depraved
And on his tombstone has engraved…

'This sad man's life at last has ended
And I've escaped unapprehended
He lay with a robot curvaceous and young
Who never complained…he was poorly hung'

Boring Maureen

Heaven preserve me from the likes of Maureen
Who's plain as a pikestaff and twice as boring
Whose serious face never cracks a smile
If I see her first I run a mile

Maureen watches all the soaps
She believes in fate and horoscopes
She has no opinions, she's poorly informed
I've plans to have her chloroformed

She doesn't go out – except to the shops
She buys cereals, veg and cheap pork chops
She avoids the clothes and the make-up aisles
Maureen has a plain life style

She doesn't drive, doesn't do sex
Never married, there is no ex
She wears no perfume, jewellery or slap
Her shoes are lace ups, black and flat

Maureen's life is passing her by
Her imagination has run dry
Her jamas are on by eight each night
She sips her Horlicks by candle light

Maureen's life is safe but stale
She runs no risk so she cannot fail
She has no fun, she has no vices,
Her parents had 'made sacrifices'

She'd been 'a disappointment' to them
Tho' she'd stayed at home to look after them
Never had nights out with her mates
And in the end she'd accepted her fate

I want to shake her but she's totally stuck
Her parents have really fucked her up
I fear there's little likelihood
Of Maureen reaching womanhood

I doubt Maureen's parents would ever admit
How they deliberately, slowly and bit by bit
Refused to let their daughter live…

To be honest I'd just about given up hope
When she tossed aside her horoscope
I caught a flame in her eye and sensed fire in her belly
She's watching 'Gogglebox' on telly!
And blow me down! That can't be right
She's swapped her Horlicks for cocoa tonight!
And check this out – she's got a chocolate digestive…
She's nibbling in a manner highly suggestive
She's wearing suspenders, her blouse is red
I dread to think what her Dad would have said

Maureen's rebelling and not before time
I heard she's found a bloke on line
Tongues are wagging she's become quite racy
She's discovered sex and rough puff pastry!

So three cheers for Maureen whose life was tough
Who's kicked the Horlicks into touch
Who's developed a taste for being naughty
Known far and wide for being saucy

Had her parents known they'd have died of shame
They'd worked so hard to keep her tame
But now they're gone, they're a thing of the past
And Maureen has grown, she's a woman at last

PLAYFUL THOUGHTS

The Cadger

He has no shame
No boundaries
No inhibitions

He sits at my husband's feet
With his ears pricked and a hopeful stare
Admiring the meal
Greedily watching every forkful from plate to mouth
Mouth to plate
Plate to mouth
Licking his chops

He is rewarded

He never sits next to me
He knows it's pointless

Even Then

My husband wants a cat.
I don't.
So I have to stay strong
I know I mustn't give in, I must not relent
Otherwise I'll spend the next 15 years wishing I hadn't
But... I feel mean and... guilty
Because I know if I wanted one *he'd* let *me*

We've had cats before
And don't get me wrong, I've loved them all
Even when they've paddled their mucky paws
Right across my kitchen floor

Even when they've slept on the washing
Pinched the chicken
Dug up the garden
Climbed the curtains
Brought a mouse
Into the house
Come in bedraggled after a fight
Woken me up in the middle of the night
Shed their hairs everywhere
Have stuck their noses in the air
And after a week in a high class cattery
Have refused to even look at me
Even then
I've loved them

So, I'm sorry
But it's a 'no' from me.
It's, 'thanks
But no thanks'

Sorry? ...pardon?
Ohhhhhh...noooo...a.a.a.ah
Awwwww... he's gorgeous!
Awwwww... go on then

What shall we call him?

Anti-biotics versus Alcohol

God, I felt bad
Awful, naff
But I picked up quick
With anti-biotics

Went on hol...
Was told
'You have to choose
Between pills and...booze'

Decisions
Decisions
But really it was no competition
Needless to say, alcohol won

Oh My God, I feel bad
Awful, naff...

The Raffle

Some bright spark on the committee suggested a raffle would raise the
necessary funds
For the trip out to somewhere that no-one except Mavis has ever heard of
But who assures us it is, 'fantastic'
And an absolute, 'must see'

That started the trend
Now, whether we like it or not, there's a raffle at every meeting
And like good girls we all buy a ticket
Because it's what the Brits do int it?
It would feel rude
To refuse

We don't need the prize
We don't want the prize
(What is it anyway?)

Nevertheless, when the tickets are drawn
We all go quiet
As we anticipate the prospect of winning

They draw the first ticket
'Oooh, it's mine
IT'S MINE!'

Heads swivel and a ripple travels around the hall,
'Who's got it?'
'It's Margaret,'
'Who?'
'Margaret,'
'Margaret?'
 'Didn't she win it last time?'
'I never win'
'Makes you think, I say, it makes you think'
'Yeah.'

Margaret, wearing a sly smile
And accompanied by hypocritical applause
Limps her way to the front
To claim her prize
A pot plant
Which, the rest of the members bitterly assert
Wasn't their cup of tea anyway.

Sod's Law

We learned a lesson yesterday:-
I.e. Make a careful note of where you park
Note a few land marks
And don't make it a tree
'Cos one tree looks very much like another tree

Take the time to look around
Which level you're on and whereabouts
Because it'll save you hours later on

I offer you this advice for free
It comes as a result of bitter experience
Of trudging for two hours around seven huge car parking areas

Until someone kindly pointed us in the direction of an 8th
Hidden from view
And one we considered we certainly hadn't parked upon
But we thought, 'worth a try, nothing to lose'
And there it was, our little car!
Hurrah!

Ever positive I said, 'well we've had a nice day and the rain's held off
And ever positive, I jumped on the scales this morning
Would you believe it – sod's law
I hadn't lost a fucking ounce!

Consolation Prize

I must have been about seven
When my sister pushed me into a competition
She shoved me up on the stage
With 20 other kids about the same age
All of **them** were excited
But I was frightened
For I knew in my gut
This would not be good.

We were all given a bag of crisps, a bottle of pop and a balloon
We had to gobble up the crisps, drink the pop then blow up the balloon
Until it burst

The other kids were magnificent
Stuffing the crisps into their mouths and drinking their pop as fast as
anything
But I'd been taught to drink slowly
And to chew my food thoroughly
Consequently
I was still eating my crisps
When all the others kids had finished

My sister, disgusted with my performance
Mimicked me from the audience
Nim nim nim nim nim nim nim …nim

Later I was forgiven
As we shared a huge bar of Cadbury's Dairy Milk
My consolation prize - for coming last

Christmas Cards in November

My first Christmas card arrived on the 23rd of November
And I wasn't pleased
Or grateful
I was angry

My first thought was...unprintable
But to sum it up in a nutshell
I thought
What's this all about?
What's she trying to prove?
Am I supposed to be impressed
With her efficiency?
Because I'm not

And I'll bet any money she'd got all her presents bought and wrapped by
October
At the latest
Well, Big Deal

Then I become thankful
Grateful
That I've got more to do with my time and energy
I'd rather run around like a headless chicken on Christmas Eve
Than be that controlled by events

I become more kindly
I think, 'Catherine, you're being mean
It takes all sorts. Wouldn't do for us all to be the same
Would it?'

And I remember my early Christmasses
Those special stockings on the end of the bed
With Imperial Leather soap and a new sponge,
An orange, an apple and a bag of nuts.

LIFE AND DEATH THOUGHTS

Numbers

Our lives revolve around numbers
Each one personal and unique
And Individual
To Something
Or Someone

National Insurance
Tax
Bank account
Bank Sort Code
Pin
It drives me mad

Car registration
Car insurance
Car Tax
Car chassis number
Car radio code
All specific and unique to YOUR car

Hospital reference number
Date of birth,
Temperature
Heart rate
Blood pressure
Number of pills
Strength of pills

Map references
Road number
House number
Telephone number
Land line and mobile
Wi fi

Sports
How fast can you run?
How high can you jump?
How far can you throw?
Goals
Handicap
P.B.
World record

You're nobody if you don't have a number
You don't exist
You can't vote
Or work…
You're not allowed to be ill
Or receive a pension
Without a number

No tomorrow

Like headless chickens we rush around like there's no tomorrow
We're ruled by the clock,
Our calendars,
Our diaries
And unrealistic expectations

We're pushed to out-perform
To break the record
To achieve

We're impatient for everything to start
And then to finish
For people to move on
Move forward
Move out of the way

We're caught in the trap of wanting everything to be faster
Trains, buses, cars, planes…
Computers…
Food…

We tap our fingers and tut as we wait for
Appointments…
Tests…
Results

But what does it all achieve
Apart from an early grave?
Where there really is
No tomorrow

Imperceptible

It was almost imperceptible at first
Little snaps and outbursts
Nothing too concerning
But somehow out of character
If you know what I mean

He'd ask, 'Now then, where are we going?'
I'd only told him minutes before…
So that was the end of the car
The beginning of the end
Of what we'd had
Of what we'd shared
For 50 years

Holidays were out of the question
He'd get disorientated and fret
He walked naked into the hotel foyer
The receptionist was 'understanding'

The home was excellent
Clean and caring
But he just didn't get it

Old age is a bitch

Death – it's a funny thing

Death you know, it's a funny thing
It catches you off guard – with your pants down,
You think, 'I'll just phone…' or 'I'll just ask…' then remember, 'Oh my God,
he's not there any more',
You've never felt so empty before

Or so full…of grief
Of shame
Of guilt

You think, 'I should have done more'
Even though there was clearly no more
To be done

You move between sadness and anger
Tears followed by rage and back again
You think, 'The bastard. How dare he leave me like this?
Bloody men!'

Time moves on
But you don't
You feel stuck
Miserable
Choked
Bloody men!

Common sense, logic, tells you things will improve
All the brochures, everybody else who's been there, tells you
It will get better
But it doesn't feel like it will
They've got it wrong

Then one day you find yourself laughing
Then you feel guilty for laughing
And shocked
That you can laugh
Again

As part of a group exercise we were asked to write about flowers. As I'm inspired by people rather than nature this was my effort.

Flowers?

Nigel Farage?
Rag wort

Boris Johnson?
Giant Hog Weed

Vladimir Putin?
Hemlock

Donald Trump?
Narcissus

Theresa May?
Artificial and grey

Jeremy Corbyn?
Mmmm – the Cats Whiskers

Andy Burnham
(I quite like him)
Chestnuts
Because they stand for justice

And finally, Jo Cox
Sunflowers, Poppies and Forget-Me-Nots

A Sad and Miserable Man

He complained every time, to everyone about everything
And without exception everyone thought
'What a fucking sad and miserable man.'

He'd get up at dawn to go to car boots
And return home fondling his new found loot
He'd beat down the vendors to the barest minimum
For a couple of quid he acquired a skeleton
What a bargain!

He'd search the supermarket for bargain buys
As he scoured the shelves he'd huff and sigh
He'd bitterly complain about the cost of a job
And argue blacks white till they came down a few bob
He hung on to his brass!

He'd walk for miles to save the odd pound
He knew the charity shops for miles around
The assistants drew straws when they saw him come in
'It's your turn today, you serve him'
Miserable git

And you'd never have guessed from the clothes he wore
That he was highly accomplished in accountancy law
That he knew the markets and invested in shares
That he'd once been married but sired no heirs
Too tight to have kids

He didn't have a telly, he would sit in the dark
He would scavenge for food in the bins in the park
He was totally obsessed with saving money
He'd do just about anything to not spend any
He was a sad and miserable man

And nobody knows and nobody cares
About the millions he made and his stocks and shares
For he had no friends and he had no heirs
He died intestate and the law declares…
That the treasury should take the lot

It will soon be over

My Mum was modest, patient and hardworking
She was there when I needed her
When I wanted her
When I was asked to play a solo at the local panto
She said, 'Good Luck and just think, 'it will soon be over.'

When I was on the labour bed
She wasn't there
But I still wanted her
And from somewhere I heard
'Just think, it will soon be over'

Something horrible happened recently
And I heard her say:
'Stick to your guns, don't give way'
So I haven't
Because one day it will be over

Parents talk you long after they're gone
You might even hear them say, 'oh, go on,'
'Trust yourself,' 'have a go,' 'have a stab'
'You know if you don't you'll wish you had,
'Cos this chance might soon be over'

Yes, parents remain powerful even in their graves
You can feel them watching when you misbehave
Offering advice and being indulgent
And from time to time passing judgement
Even though they're over

Ninety Seven

Minnie was ninety seven and smart
Very smart
She'd had a good life
An interesting life
And she loved to talk

Minnie was lovely
She retained her faculties
She could see, she could hear and she could hold an intelligent conversation
'I can't complain' she said, 'because you see, I've had a good education'

She lived in a home
A very good home
'But,' she said, 'it isn't home'

Heart to Heart
Zoe Chambers – dedication

This poem is a dedication
To the remarkable child who was Zoe Chambers
It is a tribute to the work of Dr Christaan Barnard
Who performed the very first transplant of the heart
It is also plea for organ donation
So that others like Zoe, can have the operation

It was clear to the Doctors from the very start
That Zoe had been born with a defective heart
And all of the medics quickly agreed
That their skills alone couldn't meet her needs

For 100 days (the maximum allowed)
Zoe survived with an artificial heart
Her family pleaded to the world at large
'Someone please help, Zoe needs a new heart'

And in the nick of time a match was found
Zoe had the operation and she laughed and she bounced
She was pink, she was brave, she was cheeky, she was bold
Little Zoe Chambers broke the mould

It's thanks to the donor and Dr Christiaan Barnard
That Zoe received the gift of a heart
That for one whole year she had a family life
For without that op she could not have survived.

Zoe's life was tragically short
But she left a legacy that endures
For her memory and the work of Dr. Christiaan Barnard
Might you consider donating your heart?
And as you sign the form remember Zoe Chambers
That special child who is flying with the angels.

Down the Drain

Olivia's best friend is her mobile phone
It sleeps by her side so she's never alone
She doesn't go out, she sits on her bum
She piling on weight, just like her mum

From dawn till dusk she taps away
Her facial expression more blank every day
She's no personality, she makes no effort
She has no job, and no work ethic

She has no ambition, no drive, no umph
No aspirations, no push, no punch
At doing nothing she's become a master
Her social life is a pure disaster

She's always tired, she's always ill
Her interaction is practically nil
And I feel quite sorry but I also feel mad
That she won't grow up and face the facts

It's frustrating to watch a young life like that
Drift to nothing when she should be glad
Because she should be proud, she should be bouncing
She should be clubbing, she should be flouncing

But it's not going to happen and that's hard to take
Her friends are all virtual not face to face
And I feel so helpless and I feel such pain
As another young life slips down the drain

Tip of the Iceberg

I'm upset
No, more than that, I'm angry
Fuming, actually
At the injustice
Of our so-called 'system'
Which appears to work from the outside
Until it lets you down from the inside

Windrush
Shipman
Gosport
These are not isolated cases

Tip of the iceberg if you ask me

Haiku

I just want to scream
I was enjoying my life
Then it was gate crashed

TWO PROSY THOUGHTS

So you think you'd like to keep bees?

If you're considering bee keeping as a hobby I would seriously advise you to think again. And then again.

My advice, after 9 years, is the following.

Ignore anyone who tells you it's easy – it isn't - they are lying. It's complicated.

Ignore anyone who tells you it's a cheap – it isn't - they are lying. It costs a bomb.

Ignore anyone who says it isn't time consuming - it is - they are lying.

Ignore anyone who tells you it doesn't interfere in your everyday life – it does and they are lying

Finally, ignore anyone who tells you that your own bees won't sting. It's a myth - I know it's a myth because I just made it up.

If you decide to keep bees you can wave goodbye to those long summer holidays because they'll misbehave the minute you turn your back. This usually involves swarming just as friends arrive for lunch or you're about to pop out to the shops.

On the other hand it is hugely rewarding to collect those nectar points from your neighbours as they gaze admiringly through their closed patio doors and breathe audible sighs of relief as you expertly drop the swarm into a box.

I'm telling you this because nobody told us. Frankly, if they had I probably wouldn't have believed them. It's a bit like having children – you always think your own will be different. That belief keeps the human race producing and bee keepers continuously struggling, tearing their hair out and questioning their practise.

Beekeepers do the job for three main reasons. 1. It is a fascinating hobby 2. They are helping the environment and 3. They hang on to the hope that they will eventually reap the financial rewards by selling their wonderful products at top notch prices.

The first two reasons are both real and honest but I feel it's important to be clear on that last point. It's not going to happen. This is not is a money-making hobby. Definitely not. We've decided after 9 years of learning, paying out and riding an emotional roller coaster to accept this is nothing more than a very interesting but very expensive pass time. To date our costs top £2000 and we've produced 53 jars of honey. You do the math. We're hopeful of producing more this year. One day maybe 10 years or so from now we might just about break-even but we're not banking on it. But there, I've said it, 'we're hopeful'. We need to be.

As for selling the stuff? For the most part you can forget it. Friends and relatives expect you to give it away. After all, I give my jam and marmalade away so why would honey be any different? Neighbours need to be wooed with it. You literally need to keep them sweet. They may not take kindly to bees swarming into their garden when they're about to take advantage of a sunny afternoon and are planning a barbeque in the evening. (We are lucky with our neighbours, they're brilliant).

'Well, what about your local deli?' I hear you ask. 'Surely they'd be glad to take some local honey and sell it for you?' Yes, indeed they probably would when you've found your way around the legalities of it. Labelling and such like. Those obstacles are surmountable if you're determined enough and have the time and inclination to go about it. But it's a minefield. I tell you it's a minefield.

These are the facts. I'm telling you the truth. Before you make your final decision on whether or not to go ahead try talking to a few people who blithely say, 'oh yes, I used to keep bees.' Don't leave it there. Dig deeper. Be persistent. Ask them why they stopped? And, believe them.

On the upside you do make friends. Very good friends. Which is unsurprising really because they all think you'll give them a jar of your honey that up to now has cost you approximately £50 a jar to produce.

I thoroughly recommend bee keeping as a wonderful hobby to all the people I know and love. I also recommend it to the people I can't stand.

Free to Good Home

My son took me out for a little trip today. We went to The Moors - or was it
The Dales? No. I'm sure it was The Moors – not that it really matters.
We enjoy our days out together. When they happen, that is.

'Be ready by 7.00,' he'd said, 'that'll give us plenty of time.'

I had my jacket and shoes on by 6.30 and I'd prepared us a pack up.
Tuna sandwiches, a tin of peaches and some carnation milk I'd found at the
back of the cupboard. And a MASSIVE flask of tea. He doesn't get fed like
that at home. But he seems happy enough.

He arrived at 10.00. He'd got the time wrong. Apologised. Funny thing was
he thought he was early, he thought it was 11.00 not 7.00. Maybe it was.
I do get a bit mixed up sometimes. He said he was taking me out somewhere
special for lunch and I shouldn't have bothered packing up. Good job really
because I'd already eaten my sandwiches with him being so late. I'm sure he
said 7.00.

Anyway, he helped me into the car and off we went. He drives like the wind.
I was grateful when we got stuck behind a lorry because it slowed him down.
He got all wound up and tried to pass. He gets something called 'road rage'.
I told him there was no rush.

He chatted away about this and that. I can't remember a lot of what he said,
it was just nice to have his company and hear his voice. And he made me
laugh. Ooh, he did make me laugh. And I could do with a few more of those
these days. The tricks he gets up to – it's nobody's business. Yes, he's one on
his own, as they say.

Except he's not.

His wife... and kids. They're a drain. She's a miserable bugger if ever I met
one. Never seen her crack her face. And the kids. It's all want, want, want.
My mum used to have a saying, 'I want never gets'. They think different.
They think if they don't ask they don't get. And they never fail to ask.
'Can I have? Can I have?' I've told him – just say 'no' but he never does.
If those kids ask for something, anything – they get it. It was different in
my day. And it never did me any harm.

I don't get invited any more.

We'd been travelling for a bit when he said, 'we're going somewhere different today Mum. I've been checking a few places out. I wanted to find somewhere really nice. It's only about 50 miles so it won't take us long.'

'I said, 'I hope it's not expensive' and he just laughed. Just laughed.

I was glad I'd eaten those sandwiches earlier because otherwise I'd have been starving. I'd got some sweets in my bag. I always carry some because you never know. Caramels. I love a caramel. I offered him one. He said, 'you open it for me,' so I did.

Neither of us could talk for a few minutes.

We seemed to have been travelling for a long time and the views were lovely but I needed a pee. I didn't like to complain because this was a special treat but eventually I had to ask, 'are we nearly there yet?'

He laughed, 'that's what we used to say when we were going on holiday. Do you remember?'

I said, 'of course I remember.' But I didn't.

Things went quiet. We both seemed a bit lost for words and I was concentrating on not wetting myself – which wasn't easy. I had to keep telling myself to just hang on.

I started getting upset. It annoyed him but I couldn't help it. He's never been good with emotion. I needed to get out of the car, I was absolutely busting. So I asked him to stop for a minute so I go behind a bush.

He was horrified, he said 'You can't do that. It's broad daylight. What are you thinking?' And he refused to stop. Refused to stop. My son.

I blame her…his wife.

I managed to hang on – well just about. I made my mind up not to go out with him again. I'd rather stay at home and watch the telly than risk this. It was too much.

So I was in a bit of a state when we finally arrived. I more or less fell through the door. To my son's embarrassment I stumbled past a couple of others at the reception and asked where the toilet was. They gave me a sort of 'understanding' look and pointed across the corridor. Thank God.

But wouldn't you just know it, there was a queue. You can practically guarantee there'll be a queue when you're busting.

I got myself sorted. I always carry a spare pair, just in case. I met my son again in reception. I got a shock to see his wife was there too. Val. 'Hello, Mum,' she smirked. Voice, sugary sweet. She's never called me 'Mum' in all the years I've known her. And I've never wanted her to. I'm sure I didn't look pleased to see her because I wasn't.

And it unsettled me – seeing her. Made me wonder what was going on? The lady behind the desk smiled and asked rather too brightly, if 'I'd had a good journey, dear?' My son answered for me, 'Yes, thanks'.

I am capable of speaking for myself.

I suddenly felt very wary. I took a slow look around. This was not a hotel or a nice little tea shop in the country. I'd been caught out by my own son and his bitch of a wife. What was worse I hadn't got a clue where I was. And I couldn't run – not with my knees.

Now, I'm well aware I can be a bit forgetful. More so lately, I'll admit. But I usually get there in the end. And today, thankfully, I was having a good day. Which was fortunate because I knew I needed to have my wits about me. I wasn't ready for this. Not by a long chalk.

Clearly they thought otherwise. They're worried about their future. Their future. Not mine. They're scared I'll become a burden. A few little mistakes and a couple of appointments missed here and there and they're panicking I might start relying on them. I might start taking up some of their valuable time.

I knew I needed to be careful if I was going to outsmart them. I decided to teach them a lesson they wouldn't forget. I'd teach them to underestimate me.

So, I smiled my sweet old lady smile and gently eased myself into the biggest arm chair in reception. 'Well,' I said, 'this is a lovely place.' Everyone smiled back. 'Yes, lovely, very nice. Very comfortable. Do you think I could possibly have a look at the menu whilst I wait to be seated?'

My daughter in law froze. 'Something wrong, dear?' I asked. She couldn't speak.

My son blurted, 'Mum, what do you think this is? Why do you think I've brought you here?'

I remained innocent. 'Why, for lunch of course. And, do you know, today I wouldn't say 'no' to a glass of wine. White if you don't mind. Large. Whilst I'm waiting. That would be lovely. Thank you'

And I got my wine. The receptionist buckled to and organised it. She was clearly flummoxed. 'Not my problem,' I thought.

And I got my lunch. I told them I was disappointed with it even though it was actually pretty good. But that's not the point is it? I wasn't about to let them bulldoze me into something we'd never even had a conversation about. I'd have remembered that for sure. I couldn't believe they'd been so insensitive. They hadn't considered my feelings or recognised that for the most part I'm mainly O.K. And I like my own space. It might get lonely at times but it's my space. Of course, it used to be mine and Stan's. Now, I'm going to start getting upset if I'm not careful. But he would have agreed with me. He'd have said, 'hang on in there girl.' He was a lovely man.

So I did. I hung on. I continued to play the innocent all day long. I kept up my smiling act. I did a good job. I knew it was important. I smiled at the staff, I smiled at the residents, I smiled, smiled, smiled. All day. When they offered to show me around I smiled. I said it was very kind of them but that it really wasn't necessary. I explained I was tired because I'd been up for a long time as I'd expected my son at 7.00 o'clock this morning. I refused to budge on my 'belief' that this was simply a nice trip out for lunch with my son… and daughter in law. Now there is a burden.

I asked Rob to take me home after a couple of hours. He knew he was beat. He had the grace to look ashamed. She almost choked on the caramels in the car. If only.

I maintained my 'nice old lady' act all the way home. Stan would have been proud of me. Bless him. I chatted on about the disappointing lunch. I passed comment on the number of old people wearing slippers and joggers that didn't fit. I said, 'You'd think they'd take a bit more pride in their appearance wouldn't you, being out for lunch and that? You know, like I do.' I passed comment on the loud volume on the television. That shouldn't happen in a hotel. But weren't the staff exceptional? They couldn't do enough for you. Very kind. Nothing was too much trouble. They went out of their way. Unlike some I could mention.

They didn't say much.

We were almost home when I noticed a drive with a child's swing placed at the end it with a notice stuck on it. It said, 'Free to good home.' 'Look at that,' I said. 'Free to good home. A swing. Fancy that'

They didn't answer. Never said a word.

We drove on. At the gate I thanked them for going to all that trouble and taking me such a long way only to be disappointed by the lunch. I said what a nice surprise it had been to see Val already there when I arrived. What a treat. I said it didn't really matter about the lunch it had just nice to be with the two of them. Not.

I couldn't wait to get into my little house. I told Rob there was no need to come in with me. That I was perfectly alright. He didn't argue. She was stoney-faced. I maintained my dignity as I walked to the door and unlocked it. I turned to wave goodbye, but they'd already gone.

They thought they could pull the wool over my eyes. Not yet my dears. Not yet. The ball's still in my court.

Now, I'm just going to pour myself another glass of wine then I'm going root out that Clarice Cliff jug and that old diamond ring. Tomorrow I'll get George to come round and help me put them up for sale on ebay. We'll use the proceeds to have a bloody good day out together.

We met at the bridge club and we get on like a house on fire. He makes me laugh. He makes me laugh.

TRUMPED UP THOUGHTS

Look Out!

Look out everybody here comes Trump
With his fake news, stories and love of guns
The man who's got his finger on the button
That BIGGER THAN YOURS… dangerous…red…button

The man who, following the shootings in schools,
Has completely rewritten the book of rules
He aims to arm the teachers with guns
Now then everybody, won't that be fun?
Especially for those teachers who have fooled the board
And have certain personality flaws

Take, for example, those who are prejudiced
Or have psychopathic tendencies
Towards kids with disabilities
Or hail from ethnic minorities

Teachers who, should they see red mist,
Won't hesitate to blow those kids
To bits

But, there's no need to worry because
There's a strong and stable genius in The Whitehouse
And it's beyond the realms of possibility
That anyone with a problem personality
Could ever reach a position of such authority

Isn't it?

America - Land of the Free

America – land of the free
Not any more

Years ago people travelling to America
Failed to register
And the police turned a blind eye
Never questioned, 'who or why?'

Now millions of 'undocumented illegal immigrants'
Are being held in camps
They've been arrested
And will be deported
Good people whose only crime is to want a better life for their family
And I have to ask, 'Where's the compassion, where's the humanity?'

Racism and greed
Is on the increase

I won't be visiting whilst The Trump administration is in power
That's consumer power

Donald Trump
The President
Is no more nor less than an embarrassment

Yes, Donald will certainly make America great again
Not

I Wants a Wall

If you think we're in a mess take a look at America
That'll make you feel better
Compared to ours their leader's still in nappies
He kicks off big time when he's not happy

He stamps his feet and shouts for his Momma,
'Momma, I wants a wall
Dem 'orrible folks won't let me build ma wall
They won't listen to me Momma
Momma, Momma'

Donald has a temper tantrum and leaves the room
He sucks his thumb like he did in the womb
He blubs, 'I'm gonna teach dem Mexicans a lesson Momma
Will you tell 'em for me momma?'

He gets angry. He jumps up and down and shouts from behind the door
'You mother fuckers, go build dat wall
I refuse to talk until you build dat wall
My name's Donald Trump, I'm The President of the United States and you
will build dat wall

Now, someone bring me a triple double cheese burger from McDonalds'

And while the rest of the world sighs
Putin smiles

Deal with It

In America there's been yet another mass shooting
(They happen almost daily, apparently 3 or more constitutes a mass
shooting)
Trump declares the shooter was 'a deranged individual with mental health
problems'
And that, 'there are a lot of people in America with mental health problems'
Well... he should know

The problem, he says, is not guns – it's people!

And the people cry out for yet more guns
'Do not stop us having guns
Guns keep us safe'
And sadly
They're serious

I tell you what Trump
Why not give all new born babies a gun?
Teach them from the cradle to the grave
That guns will keep them safe
Not their parents, not their teachers, not any of the responsible adults
around them
Guns
They're what you need to stay safe in America
Guns
Definitely

Seriously man - words fail me
Take responsibility
Take some leadership
And Deal With It
Seriously

FRIENDLY THOUGHTS

Glenys

How I wish I could garden like you
And grow my own veg to make stew
If I could cultivate my plants from seed
And identify every flower and weed
I might just be gardening like you

How I wish I were arty like you
And could distinguish my purple from blue
If my ability would even halfway stretch
To paint a picture or draw a sketch
I might just be arty like you

How I wish I could ice cakes like you
Without resorting to edible glue
That if only my lattice criss crossed
And I could basket-weave, drizzle and frost
I might just ice cakes like you

How I wish I did genealogy like you
So I knew who'd done what and with who
But my family history
Will remain a mystery
I should do genealogy like you

How I wish I could sew just like you
And could stitch my lines straight not askew
That I could buttonhole, tack and embroider
But in all of these skills I'm sadly devoid-er
So I'd best leave the sewing to you

How I wish I'd run a shop like you
And had the courage to see it through
You are truly creative
Not just decor - a - tive
How I wish I was more like you

Alice Thompson

Alice Thompson looks so sweet
A nicer person you couldn't meet
Her mild exterior, her gentle form
Her manner that is oh, so warm

Alice Thompson looks so sweet
You'd never guess what lies beneath
She raps with kids who live on the street
She sticks to the rhythm and keeps to the beat

They say 'Alice Thompson we think you're cool
If you'd been our Mum we'd have gone to school
Go on Alice – rap us another
Oh! how we wish you'd been our mother'

Alice Thompson is good with words
She writes in rhyme and speaks in verse
Her approach to life is quite diverse
She makes up poems about watching birds

Alice Thompson has got a neighbour
Who sounds to have quite challenging behaviour
He's only gone and bought a taser
But even that doesn't seem to faze her

Because Alice is tough and Alice is deep
She keeps one eye open when she goes to asleep
She isn't frightened of a taser zap
She will simply disarm him with a rap

He will discover by and by
That there's more to Alice than meets the eye
Because Alice Thompson is good with words
She writes in rhyme and she speaks in verse

Evie

My wonderful grand daughter (aged nine and three quarters)
Paid me the best compliment ever
When she asked, 'what do you want to be when you're older,
Nana?'

I smiled
And somehow controlled the urge to say…
'Alive'

But she was serious
Curious
And clearly Evie
Believed
In Me

So I whispered back, 'Evie, I want to be famous
I'm something and three quarters and I want to be famous
I need to be famous
Something inside me,
Drives me
I'm a slave
To fame'

I tell her, 'my sister was famous
And though I was proud I was just a tiny bit jealous'

She whispered, 'Nana, I want to be famous too'

And I tell her
'Evie, keep those dreams
Hold on to those dreams
Keep that light
Hold on to that light
Believe
Believe in your genes.
Because you get them from me!!
And I know you'll be famous
Eventually'

Bill Grundy

He was, as they say, one on his own

My husband, (not known for his patience)
Was remarkably patient
With his best friend, Bill Grundy

A very difficult, exasperating and exhausting man
An offensively rude if brutally, honest man
Who would tell people in no uncertain terms exactly what he thought of them

A man who would invite Jehovah's Witnesses into his home
And as he put it, 'jaw 'em to death' …
Once they'd escaped, they never came back

A man who would lose at squash to my husband every time
Nine one, nine love, nine two
But still thought he could teach him a thing or two

A man who thought he was paying me a huge compliment by saying he liked me
Because I was like him
Because I too am 'a self-opinionated big head'

A man who, quite frankly, most people found a pain in the arse
Who after 10 minutes in his company
Had had more than enough

A man I found incredibly annoying
But whose candid attitude
I found refreshing

I respected that he was unable to comprehend why anyone would take offence
When he himself never took offence at anything
I was amused by his admission that he was 'the smartest person' he knew
And his astonishment at my response that, 'he wasn't the smartest person I knew'
I liked he was proud that at seventy he could 'still stand up to put his socks on'
I admired that he woke up every day 'eager for life and ready to face the world'…
I mean… how many of us can say that?

And I was unbelievably sad when he died
It's left a gap
Because he definitely was, as they say, 'one on his own'

Ms J Sharp
There should be more like her around

That Sharpie well…she can be a bit of a…
You know…
When the occasion calls for it…
Let's just say…she don't take no shit
She simply tells it how it is

There should be more like her around

That Sharpie well…she can…
You know…
When the need arises…
Let's just say…when she's firing on all four cylinders
She's dangerous

That Sharpie well…sometimes…
You know…
In an argument…
Let's just say…she can wipe the floor with the opposition
With her vocabulary it's sheer demolition

There should be more like her around

That Sharpie well…she might seem…
You know…
Tough
But she's a heart and soul to shame all of us
She's the girl you can rely on
Should you ever need a shoulder to cry on
She's always generous and always kind
She's honest by nature and sharp of mind
She's got spirit and vitality
Courage and personality
Character and drive
Dignity and pride

There should be more like her around

An Old friend

I bumped into an old friend today
Not seen her for years
And we both agreed
We'd not changed a bit!

It made us feel good to lie
And every once in a while
You need that
A bit of a boost

We compared children
Grand children
Partners
Retirement
Health

Considered the future
Reflected on the past:

Her mantra goes:-
'I'm old enough to know better
Young enough to do it again
And wise enough not to get caught'

Sounds good to me

SERIOUS THOUGHTS

It's well over 50 years since this happened but it's one of the most resounding memories of my junior school days.

Robert Shelton got the cane

I tolerated school
I just sort of…drifted through
It came at the wrong time
Thirty years later would have suited me fine
I'd have felt ready for it then

Don't get me wrong there was nothing specific
I just wasn't ready to be serious
Five is too young to be serious about life
And eleven too young to have your life mapped out
By the Eleven Plus

Miss Latham was my junior school teacher – and she was GOOD
Prepared everyone of us as best as she could
For the Eleven Plus

Then that bastard Head Master Chamberlain
Gave Robert Shelton the cane
The memory of it is imprinted on my brain
……The thwack
……The crack

Respect for Robert he didn't cry
Nor did he pass the Eleven Plus…
Thanks to that bastard Chamberlain

Humiliation

I'm outraged

Female Grimsby Town Football Club supporters
Literally had to show their 'support'
By lifting their tops to display their bras
To all and sundry
In the name of security
At the Stevenage match on Saturday
(19 August 2017)

Bullshit

This is not security
This is humiliation
This is abuse

Some women have managed to laugh it off
I say, 'do not laugh it off
It's not a joke
It's disgusting

Be outraged
Be furious
Get revenge
Take control
And refuse to attend Stevenage again'

And real men
Will support these women
And likewise refuse to attend Stevenage again

Stevenage Football Club should be grovelling
And apologising
Unreservedly

Take a survey

It seems that these days every time I book something
Or buy something
I'm asked to complete a survey.
I'm told it helps to improve customer service.

To encourage me to complete their survey
I'm offered a bribe:-
Which consists of an entry into a prize draw
Where I stand a one in fifty thousand chance
Of winning a £50 voucher to spend on anything I like on Amazon
So naturally, I go ahead.

I'm asked to rate my purchase on a scale of one to ten
Where one is totally dissatisfied
And ten is completely satisfied

Twenty minutes in and the 'survey' subtly changes
They are no longer interested in my purchase

They would like to know my age and marital status,
My income and employment status
Do I have dependant children living at home?
Do I own my own home?
Do I have insurance?
Have I ever been refused insurance?
Do I consider myself to be disabled or ill?
Have I made a will?

And I suddenly stop and think, 'you have gone way too far
Just who on earth do you think you are?

So I go back and I painstakingly change all my answers
I say I am completely dissatisfied with the product
And that it is not fit for purpose.

I tell them I'm thirty five and survive on benefits
That I live in a rented, two bedroomed flat
With my alcoholic husband, five children and disabled mother

Needless to say
I didn't win the £50 Amazon voucher

The System

My Mum used to say, 'eat up your dinner, they'd be glad of that in Africa'
But sixty years down the line people are still starving in Africa
A juxtaposition
The filthy poor paying rent to the filthy rich to live in filthy conditions

It's The System
And you cannot beat The System

Conflict, Greed and War,
What's it all for?
And it's only luck
That it isn't us

We see the appeals on the telly
We pick up our mobiles and donate a few quid - it makes us feel better
As we eat our takeaways
Our easy meals
On our knees
In front of the telly

At the supermarket we put dried pasta in the food bank bin
Because something deep down inside us
Tells us
It's only luck that it isn't us

So, 'Eat up your dinner, they'd be glad of that in Africa
Don't you know they're starving in Africa?'

Grenfell Tower

That Fire
That unnecessary fire
That *preventable* fire
Grenfell Tower

Those people
Those poor people
Those hard working, just want to get on with their lives, normal, everyday,
family people

Those firemen
Those brave firemen
Those determined caring, courageous, tireless firemen

Those volunteers
Those generous, time giving, expertise offering volunteers
Those charitable, understanding, shattered volunteers

But those people
Those poor, desperate, traumatised people
Who will suffer for the rest of their lives
Every time they close their eyes
Every time they smell smoke
Every time they hear a scream or a child cry
Will flash back
The sights
The sounds
The smells
Having been indelibly printed on their brains
To remind them
To keep themselves safe

But that council
That unforgiveable council
That uncaring, non-listening, self serving, penny pinching, tight fisted
council
Whose chief executive frankly doesn't know his arse from his elbow
Has been forced to stand down
And not before time

His resignation shines one tiny light…
But you can rest assured
He'll sleep safe in his bed tonight

I wrote this just one day before the American, British and French made targeted strikes in Syria.

Sleeping Uneasily

Whilst we in the West have slept
Relatively easily in our beds
Putin's been cosying up to Syria
Two tyrants together in Syria
And we've done virtually nothing about it
We've been too busy arguing about Brexit
To notice

Then out of the blue comes a poisoning in Salisbury
The rather genteel, quintessentially English, Salisbury
And suddenly the West wakes up
What the fuck?
We stamp our feet, 'he's gone too far this time – we'll teach that Putin to mess with us'

Putin's response is, 'don't look at us…it's got nothing to do with us
We don't do chemical attacks
Everybody knows that
The latest one? Again, not us
Don't blame us.
It's got nothing to do with us
Stop pointing the finger at us
It isn't us
It's never been us
It's high time you in the West to grew up'
…Methinks he doth protest too much

Now, I don't know if you agree
But to me the world is growing ever more scary
I think things are getting pretty hairy
And I don't say this light heartedly
But the terrifying possibility
Is that we are heading for World War Three
Simply because they didn't confront it initially
And now ordinary people like you and me
Have to carry on as normal and wait and see
Whilst feeling helpless,
Impotent and powerless

So, I won't be sleeping easy in my bed tonight
I'm just hoping the politicians can sort it out
Mmmmmmm??

False Economy

So far as I can see
Austerity
Have been proved to be
Simple false economy
Except for a few fat cats at the top
Who don't give a monkeys whether it works or not
For whatever or which way
They'll be O.K.

They refer to the homeless
As 'No-Hopers'
As 'Alkies' and 'Druggies'
'Who,' they declare with brazen self-importance, 'are nothing like us
We've worked hard for what we've got
And we're keeping it (whether we need it or not)
'Cos it's ours
All ours'

Crime has increased
Health has decreased
Morale has declined
People feel disillusioned and disinclined
To accept austerity
As necessary

In Britain there are people dying on the streets
We're one of the richest countries in the world and people are dying on the
streets
For the want of Love
A Home
And Hope

Third and fourth generation of unemployed in a family
Whose aspirations are limited to a trip to the offy
Or a win on the lottery
Before the relief of their trip to the cemetery

It's sad, it's disgusting, it's shameful
That the poor should be made to feel grateful
For the food bank
Which, I understand,
Is the only public service where business is actually booming
And whose service is continuously improving
And it's run by volunteers
Thank God for the volunteers

Charity?
Austerity?
Obscenity

Two o'clock Girl

He was drunk the first time he called me
'A two o'clock girl'
I asked,
'What's that?'
He laughed in my face. 'You mean you don't know?'
'No,' I answered and before I could stop myself, I added,
'But I'm sure I'm about to find out'
That was when he hit me
I should have known to keep quiet

'It means, you stupid bitch, that you're not up to much'
I mumbled something and got a kick for my trouble
He ranted and raved, 'take a look at yourself, you ugly cow,
Jesus, how the fuck did I end up with you?
The last girl standing in the club at two in the morning'

Silently I thought, 'but I was still standing'

The next day he was, as usual
Remorseful
Bought me flowers
Cried, 'I'll never do it again
It's the drink talking
You know I love you, don't you?'

Silently I nodded
But those words
Those cruel words,
'Two o'clock girl' were too much
They hurt too deep
And finally I told him
'I'm leaving'

SAD THOUGHTS

Fallen Apart

She and   I   have   fall   en   a   part
          And   it's   bro
                  ken
                  my
          he   art
          It's   sad
          So   s   ad

I can't do   right   for doing   wrong
   Every   thing   is   w   ron   g
I heard   my mother say,   'stay   str   ong'

          You couldn't   make it up
I can't try   any   more   so I've given   up

          At the end of the day
       When Push comes to Shove
      She's a Woman with a Grudge
            And Enough
      Is   Enough
         Is   E   n   ough

Picking up the Pieces

Kids eh?
Drive you mad don't they?
You can't live with 'em
And you can't live without 'em
You do your best to guide 'em
But you can't tell 'em
Can yer?

And then
When
They're broken and hurting
Disbelieving, need nursing
We pick up the pieces
And put 'em back together again

He's Ours

Our grandson moved in with us recently
He's changed our lives significantly
Whereas we used to go out without a backwards glance
Now everything must be planned in advance

Logan, is slightly autistic
Which makes him very repetitive
And stubborn
Yes, he's stubborn and repetitive
Repetitive
And stubborn
But we love him
Because, well, you know, he's ours

Logan is fussy about what he'll eat
He'll accept chicken nuggets but refuse roast beef
He loves fish fingers and chips and jelly
He'll also eat yoghurt (but not raspberry)

Without a shadow of a doubt
He's the master of the house
But's that's O.K. because he's, well, you know, he's ours

Life's funny sometimes, it catches you out
When you least expect it, it all turns about
We've had to adapt, it's been pretty rough
But you know the old saying, 'when the going gets tough?'
And we're not there yet, we've a way to go
But we're making headway, and well, y'know
We love him don't we…and he's ours.

Haiku

It's getting too much
I feel like I'm going mad
Please, give me some space